It can get better

Dealing with common behaviou
children with autism

Paul Dickinson and Liz Hannah

First published 1998 (revised and reprinted 2014) by
The National Autistic Society
393 City Road
London EC1V 1NG
www.autism.org.uk

The National Autistic Society is a charity registered in England and Wales (269425
and in Scotland (SC039427) and a company limited by guarantee registered in
England (No.1205298), registered office: 393 City Road, London EC1V 1NG.

ISBN 978 1 905722 90 7
Written by Paul Dickinson and Liz Hannah
Edited by Elizabeth Ayris
Cover illustration by Steve Lockett
Designed by Cottier and Sidaway
Printed by Rap Spiderweb

Contents

Acknowledgements

Thanks to everyone who has helped us prepare this booklet. Thanks especially to Steve for his wonderful drawings and his patience while we've both struggled to get this done in between all the other things we try and do. Thanks to Jacquie Turner who read through a draft script from a parent's perspective and also to Mrs D Turnbull-Justice.

We also thank The National Autistic Society for agreeing to print and publish our work and for supporting our aim of trying to produce something useful for parents.

Above all, thanks to the children we have worked with, and their parents who first put to us that writing this was something we should do.

Introduction

When we originally decided to write this book, there was very little information available for parents and carers to help them understand and comfort a child with autism.[1] Children with autism can be delightful, rewarding, loving and fun to be with, but they can also present challenges to parents in the way they experience and comprehend the world around them. Additionally, they may struggle to communicate what they want or to understand what others want from them, especially in the early years, and sometimes throughout their lives.

What we did was write a simple 'starter' book for parents of young children with autism that we hoped would be easy to read and easy to follow, with a little humour thrown in. As parents often say, 'We are given the diagnosis then left to get on with it. But it can be hard, and not what we expected'. Families frequently struggle to find the right advice for their child's particular problems. Some themes are ongoing: trials over toilet training, children not sleeping, long-lasting temper tantrums, obsessive rituals that can seem to enslave families, and sometimes frustrations that are expressed by frightening acts of self-injury.

There is now a wide variety of books available for parents and professionals covering all aspects of autism, and many sites on the internet that can help with advice. It is possible these days to make contact with other parents via the web and learn from their experiences. However, it is also useful to look something up in a book, to have it available to refer to and to make you feel a little less alone. It is important that parents do not feel they have

[1] In this book we use the term autism to refer to diagnoses on the autism spectrum, including Asperger syndrome and high-functioning autism.

to struggle on until their child's behaviour patterns become very well established and hard to change. Face-to-face professional help may be hard to find but written information is available in many forms: leaflets, booklets, in-depth studies and websites can all help. Courses (for example the EarlyBird programme[2]), parent support groups, even online study courses if you have the time, can all be supportive and informative and will help to smooth your daily life.

We do not claim to possess expertise that will enable you to respond to every difficult situation you may find yourself in. Finding a solution to a problem will be very much about what works for your family and your situation. What we have tried to do in this book is to pull together tips and ideas that have helped people in our respective work over the years. We have also sought to share the practical ways of coping that parents we have known have come up with themselves – and then shared generously with us, and also with others who are going through similar experiences. These are things that cannot be read in any professional textbook, but come from the unique experience of being the parent or carer of a child with autism.

We hope this booklet helps you to feel more positive about your ability to respond to the challenges that go with being the parent of a child with autism.

[2]For more information about the EarlyBird programme, which is offered by licensed teams in the UK and internationally, see www.autism.org.uk/earlybird.

Why does my child do things that are difficult to understand and manage?

All young children can sometimes present behaviour that puzzles or challenges the adults caring for them. However, children with autism may be harder to understand and not so easy to calm. The reasons for this are tied in with their autism, and the greater your understanding of this, the easier it will be to figure out why your child can become inconsolable, angry, anxious or confused.

Autism is complex, but it is important when trying to change behaviour that you have some understanding of **why** that behaviour has occurred, because a satisfactory solution can then be found more easily. On the other hand, some solutions are hard to find, so a sense of balance and support from friends and family are also important.

Autism is a spectrum, which means it affects children in different ways, ranging from very mild to quite severe. However, all people with autism tend to have some difficulties in the following areas.

Communication difficulties

A child may:
- have a total lack of desire to communicate at all, by gesture or sound
- communicate their needs by pushing or pulling an adult but won't point or use eye contact to share information
- sometimes echo what they hear (echolalia) but not extend this, although they may use echoed phrases correctly
- not be able to read facial expression and tone of voice

- pick up key words, or the first word in the sentence, but not the meaning behind it (eg does not understand why hitting another child is not acceptable)
- only talk about their own interests and find it hard to hold a balanced two-way conversation.

Difficulties with social understanding and social interaction

A child may:
- prefer to be alone or only with a trusted and familiar adult
- have difficulty sharing toys, taking a turn, or waiting for things to happen
- be too rough with other children and push them away or snatch things from them
- not pick up or understand unspoken social rules, for example you don't remove your clothes in a public place or speak to strangers
- not understand other people's needs or feelings
- have little awareness of their own safety or the safety of others
- always want things to go their way and feel very anxious about this.

Difficulties coping with change

Many children with autism dislike change to their daily routine, their surroundings, the people who care for them, the way their toys are organised, their clothes and so on. They want to maintain things in exactly the same way all the time. Road detours, a change of plans, different food brands, or nursery being closed can feel like the end of the world for them.

Repetitive behaviour or a narrow range of interests

Children with autism will have certain repetitive behaviour that can become compulsive, for example wanting to watch a particular part of a DVD over and over; always wanting the same computer program; insisting on eating food in a certain way; lining up toys, cushions or clothes pegs and becoming upset if they are touched by another person. There may be physical 'tics' like spinning round, finger flicking or rocking back and forth, or verbal tics where a child repeats a sound, word or phrase over and over.

Difficulties in play

Sometimes, children with autism may not understand what toys are for. They may line them up or spin the wheels but get stuck at this 'sensory motor' stage of play and need help to develop pretend and imaginative play. They sometimes confuse fact and fiction or build their play on familiar scenarios they have seen in games or DVDs. This means that they may need more support from an adult in the activities they take part in throughout the day, in order to develop.

Sensory difficulties

Many children with autism process sensory input in a different way to 'neurotypical' people (people who don't have autism). For example, you may know that your child hears certain sounds very well but they may, at times, appear to be unable to hear at all. Or they may plug their fingers in their ears because certain sounds are painful for them.

Children may love the texture of certain objects but refuse to wear new clothes because their brain processes the feeling of the new fabric as scratchy and painful. For the same reason they may only eat soft food or a narrow range of food, and it may have been difficult to wean them onto solids.

You may find that a child with autism sometimes refuses to be near certain people because they are sensitive to the smell of their perfume or the colour of their clothes. Colours and lines may move when the child looks at them, making creative activities difficult. Your child may also refuse to wear certain colours or go near items that are painted in particular colours.

Children with autism may seem over-active or under-active. This can also be a sensory response. Our proprioceptive sense tells us where our bodies are in space so we can use our limbs without thinking about it (for example, we intuitively work out how hard to press on paper when writing, or how to move our arms and legs when climbing stairs). Children whose proprioceptive sense is out of kilter may want to chew or tear things, or seek out big bear hugs and rough play. They may press too hard or too lightly with a pencil when learning to write because they can't sense the correct pressure.

Helping your child at home: some general ideas

Any parent who has a child with a disability will soon realise that a little more thought, planning and preparation may be needed to make day-to-day life go smoothly. When you have other children and/or a full-time job, this can become a process of juggling priorities. You may find that these strategies can help.

- Choose your battles. Don't struggle with things that are not very important in the long term. Your house and child may not be perfect, but you will enjoy life a lot more.
- Put aside some time each day to play or sing with your child just for fun. It will help their social and communication skills, and let you both spend some time laughing together.
- Ask for help if you need it. If help isn't available keep asking. Resources are scarce but people who are very determined get the most help! Try to see professionals with another adult so that you don't forget anything and you feel supported.
- If you are trying to tackle something big, whether it is bedtime, toileting, shopping or tantrums, break it down into manageable steps. Take it stage by stage and concentrate on one step at a time.
- Be patient, be consistent and don't give up. Decide what you are going to do and stick to it for six to eight weeks. Make sure that other people who are with your child, including school staff, grandparents and friends know what your plans are and how they can support you.
- Don't worry if things get worse to begin with. That is a normal reaction when children want things to stay the same and try harder to see that they do. Suddenly, you will find things have improved!
- It may help to keep a diary and write in it from time to time. It is reassuring to look back and see that progress has been made. Because it happens slowly, it is sometimes easy to forget what things were like at the beginning.
- The strategies you decide to use will depend on your child and your family situation. You have to choose a plan that is realistic

and is not going to cause you more upset and frustration than the behaviour you are trying to change.

- Think carefully about activities, items of food and other things your child really enjoys and use these as rewards and distractions. Changing your child's behaviour can be difficult at times but it is enormously rewarding when progress is made.
- Think about the future. Do you want your child to be doing this when they are five years older? Some things are more easily tackled when your child is young.

1. Dealing with meltdowns

Introduction

Many children have tantrums when they are young, usually around two years old when they realise they have a will of their own.

With so many confusing things to contend with, a child with autism may become very distraught at times. You may not know what your child wants or what the problem is. You might also feel embarrassed, especially if you are out and it feels as though the whole street is watching you, or you're at home in a small flat with neighbours close by. At the same time, your child sounds in great distress, you want them to stop and you may feel inadequate about not being able to manage them and keep them happy. The result is often that the child gains a lot of attention and learns that by having a tantrum, they will finally get what they want. Sometimes your child may learn that having a tantrum has interesting results – maybe everyone starts running around or offering them treats. This can make a tantrum become a 'fun' activity.

Children have temper tantrums for a number of reasons so, when looking for the best solution, try and understand why your child is behaving in this way. It may be something obvious, for example they once had chocolate while out shopping so now they want it every time. If it is not so obvious, or your child has a lot of tantrums for a number of reasons, try writing down all the situations in which they occur for a couple of weeks. Note the time of day, what triggered the behaviour and what happened as a result. Then look at all the information you have gathered and see if there is any pattern. What you want to find out is what your child gains by having a tantrum. When you know this, you can look for a way of dealing with it successfully.

A tantrum is a form of communication

If your child is unable to speak it can be frustrating for the whole family as it is so hard to know whether they are in pain, needing something or finding something uncomfortable.

If your child is at nursery, at school or seeing a speech therapist you may be given a set of symbols to help them express their needs. Symbols are simple line drawings with a word underneath, and they support communication. It can take several months for a child to understand that these drawings have meaning but when they do grasp the concept and learn to recognise the symbols, it can be a powerful aid to communication. Start by showing a symbol of what you think your child might want, and build upon this by offering a choice of two symbols, then three and so on.

If symbols are too hard for your young child to understand, photos, wrappers, or logos cut out and stuck on card can all be used. Symbols are also a useful way of showing your child what is going to happen and in what order, a strategy that can prevent many tantrums.

Although symbols are a long-term strategy, and one that requires quite a bit of effort, they are invaluable and a can save a lot of upset. If your child's nursery or school cannot provide sets of symbols, ask a speech therapist (if you are in touch with one) what they think would be suitable. Sturdy sets of symbols attached to a keyring can be found online at www.amazon.co.uk.

On a more general note, if your child has communication difficulties it is important to use short sentences and emphasise the main words. Gestures can also help if used consistently, and you have your child's attention.

Using a help card

You may have noticed that your child has a tantrum when something does not work as expected, for example the computer freezes, or a wheel drops off their favourite toy. Try teaching your child to ask for help. This is a long-term strategy, but potentially a very useful one.

Have a 'help' symbol (usually a drawing of an outstretched hand, but it can be anything as long as it is used consistently) and teach your child to hand it to you it when things go wrong. If you have noticed that they have a tantrum when a toy battery runs out, practise using the symbol by taking the battery out of the car (unseen) before giving it to your child to play with; your child will try to start it. As they begin to get upset, hand them the help card and say 'You need help.' Prompt your child to give you the help card and in exchange, reinsert the battery.

You will need to practise this, very quickly at first, until your child can hand the card to you independently, but you'll find it has many uses. If your child has older siblings, they may also be willing to spend a few minutes each day helping to teach this skill in different contexts.

If tantrums occur when your child is told 'No!'

It is difficult for all young children to understand why they can't have everything they want. It is even more difficult for children with autism to understand, particularly when life is so unpredictable to them.

As an example, your child may sometimes have a chocolate bar for a treat – but at other times that treat is not available or not allowed. On these occasions it is very important to be consistent. It is tempting (and will sometimes be necessary) to give in because you are tired, everybody is staring, and you just want to get away as quickly as possible. However, try to work out a strategy in advance and stick to it.

- Don't be angry or punish your child for their behaviour; it will make the situation more difficult and won't solve the problem in the long run. Try to keep calm and give lots of praise when your child is calmer.
- If possible, you could try to distract your child. However, children with autism can be extremely difficult to distract when they particularly want something. For them it is the most important thing in their world at that time. Distraction can work well if you are able to predict a tantrum or see the signs and jump in with a distraction before a meltdown begins.
- Try not to say 'no'. Offer other choices, or show pictures or symbols of what is going to happen instead.
- Sometimes you may have to ignore the tantrum if you can. Don't feel guilty or feel that you are a terrible parent because your child is screaming and sobbing for something you have said they can't have. Reassure your child and keep them safe

- Remember if you give them what they want and it is not safe, suitable or convenient at the time, they will think that they can have whatever they want by screaming for it. Always give your child a big cuddle at the end of a tantrum and praise for being calm.

When going to the shops or into town, your child may find the experience tiring, as they will be processing a lot of colours, smells and sounds that could be overwhelming and possibly lead to a tantrum. Here are some strategies you can try.

- If you can avoid doing a big shop with your child, and just go on short shopping trips to begin with, this can help build up their ability to cope.
- A little preparation can also help, for example, you could try bringing a reward from home to give to your child when things are beginning to get too much for them. You could also take a toy or book that acts as a distractor, and make sure you have a familiar drink available.
- You could show your child pictures of what you need to buy so they understand that treats are not on the list. (This will only work for short shopping lists, not major shopping.)
- If you want to buy crisps or sweets, you can save them for home by using a 'wait' symbol (see page 18). In that way, your child won't expect these treats to be a routine part of a shopping expedition.
- If your child thinks that passing a fast food outlet without buying anything is the end of the world, it may be necessary to have a specific symbol with a cross drawn through it. Show it to your child before you go out and say, for example,

'No McDonald's today. Supermarket then home.' Pictures of 'supermarket' and 'home' can also be shown. Repeat this several times before you leave. For a few weeks or even months it may be a good idea to avoid going in to McDonald's and similar places altogether. Or, if your child is able to understand, you could mark a day on a simple calendar when they know they will be getting that particular treat.

Using a 'wait' symbol

Children with autism can find waiting very difficult because a five-second wait, to them, can seem like an eternity. They can find it hard to imagine, if something isn't available immediately, that it might be available in the future.

A wait symbol can be an enormous help in many situations until your child understands that the spoken word 'Wait' doesn't mean 'It's never going to happen'. Wait symbols are usually red oval or circular pieces of card with the word WAIT written on them in large letters.

Start by holding something your child really wants (bubbles for example). When they reach for it, you say 'wait!' and hand them the wait card. Count for two seconds, then say 'Good waiting!' and blow the bubbles.

Gradually increase the waiting time. You may be able to use a timer to increase the time beyond a minute. Usually, by the time your child can wait calmly for ten minutes, they understand the concept of waiting and can wait for much longer, maybe an hour or two.

This is another technique that siblings may enjoy practising for a short time each day.

Similarly, if you are trying to stop your child playing in the toilet bowl but moving them away always becomes a battle, you could try the following strategies.

- Keep the bathroom door locked with a simple hook lock (though this is no good for toilet training or if your children use the toilet independently).
- If a lock is impractical, offer access to water play in a fun way, with bubbles, coloured water and bath toys. Say 'You want water play' and take your child from the bathroom to a more suitable spot in the kitchen or outdoors to play with water.
- If your child likes turning on taps and leaving them running, try bowls of water and jugs, toy watering cans, or plastic bottles with holes punched in the bottom.
- You could try other sensory play such as corn flour and water that can be coloured with food dyes and has interesting textures.
- Try making a simple picture schedule of daily activities, so that your child can see when they can have water play and what they should be doing at other times.

If you can structure your child's day and manage both your expectations and theirs, you should find that life gradually gets calmer.

If tantrums occur when your child wants to avoid something unpleasant

Because of the sensory difficulties of children with autism, and the difficulties they can have understanding everyday processes and procedures, your child may find things like bathing, nail cutting or trips to unfamiliar places very frightening or challenging. The best way to tackle these issues is to break them down into very small steps and do as much preparation as possible.

For example, your child may have a tantrum in order to avoid having a bath. In this case it is best to work out a routine that suits you and follow it every day. Keep the bath short at first and reward your child afterwards by giving them an activity or food reward they enjoy. If you think your child is really frightened of the bath, break the process down into small steps. Here is an example.

- Week 1: a quick strip-wash by the basin. (If it is summer, you could also gently encourage water play in the garden at suitable opportunities.)
- Week 2: stand in the empty bath for a few minutes with a favourite toy or treat, then get out and have a quick strip-wash.
- Week 3: have a quick strip-wash while standing in the empty bath.
- Week 4: put a small amount of water in the bath and have a quick wash.
- Weeks 5, 6 and 7: increase the amount of water in the bath and the amount of time spent in the bath.

Another common example of sensory difficulties is when a child is frightened of household sounds like the hoover, and screams when they see it appearing. If this happens with your child, it may be that the sound of the hoover really hurts their ears, so you could try hoovering when your child is at school or at nursery. If that is not practical, tackle the problem in small steps.

- Week 1: get the hoover out every day but don't turn it on. Push it round the floor for a short time, gradually increasing the time you push it.
- Week 2: encourage your child to play with or touch the hoover when it is switched off. Try putting headphones or earplugs on your child when the hoover is out, and see if they will tolerate these.
- Week 3: let your child watch their favourite DVD or do an activity they really enjoy (with headphones if possible), and turn on the hoover briefly. Do this several times a day to see how your child copes.
- If they respond well, gradually increase the time the hoover is on.

This type of step-by-step procedure can be very effective and will eventually result in success, although you will have to adapt the timeframes to suit your own child's needs.

If your child uses tantrums to gain adult attention

It is unusual for very young children who have autism to use tantrums in order to gain adult attention. This is because they often do not crave attention or seek it out, so it is more likely that the tantrum is their way of saying 'I don't like this one bit!'

If your child does like adult attention – and you always respond to their tantrums by cajoling, shouting, rewarding or punishing – you are giving them a lot of attention. It doesn't matter to your child that you may be angry; they have simply learnt that if they want your immediate, undivided attention, all they have to do is scream.

If you think this may be the problem, you could try the following strategies.

- Instead of giving your child attention when they are having a tantrum, give lots of praise when they are behaving well or playing quietly.
- If your child is having a tantrum, check thoroughly that something is not causing discomfort or frustration then say in a firm, quiet voice. 'I'm going to ignore you when you scream'.
- Turn your back, carry on doing something else, wash the dishes or just look the other way. Your child may try to gain your attention by pulling at your clothes, kicking or hitting you or being destructive. If this is impossible to ignore, tell the child calmly that they are going to their room (or any safe place) until they have calmed down. Then leave them. You can always listen at the door to make sure they are OK.
- Give lots of praise and comfort when the tantrum is over.
- If the tantrums began after the birth of a new baby, make sure that you involve your child as much as possible in helping you care for the baby. Give lots of praise for helpful and good behaviour. Try to find some time each day to spend with your older child doing something special you can enjoy

together. It is also important to encourage visitors to give attention to older children and not only to the baby.

When you have no idea why your child is so upset

It is always distressing when the child you love and care for is screaming for no obvious reason. In this situation you could ask the following questions.

- Are there loud or unfamiliar noises, movements or smells that could be causing distress? Or is your child wearing new clothes, experiencing new textures and finding things unpredictable? (See the explanation of sensory issues on page 9.)
- Has something changed? Did you take a different route to get somewhere, move a favourite toy, run out of a particular brand of cereal or rearrange the furniture? (See the section on coping with change, page 8.)
- Is your child hungry or thirsty? Try offering drink and food and see if that helps.
- Is your child overtired? (See chapter 3.)
- Is your child in pain, ill, or constipated? Try to take their temperature and think about other clues to their general health, for example, have they been rubbing one ear, have they been off their food, are they pale and listless? If you are really worried ring NHS Direct or your GP.
- Are you in an unfamiliar place or a situation that your child may find frightening? Children with autism sometimes have fears and phobias about everyday things like birds, dogs, quiet woods (if they live in the city), noisy roads, balloons, bubbles and so on. The best way to cope with fears like this is to take

a long-term view: show your child pictures, talk about it together, try something that is similar but not the same. Build up exposure to the frightening things slowly and with lots of reassurance and rewards. All young children have fears, and hopefully, with a sympathetic and supportive approach, they will outgrow them.

It is not possible to give all the answers in a short book, but hopefully the examples and ideas we have given here will be a useful guide.

2. Toileting problems

Introduction

Dr Christopher Green, who wrote the popular book, *Toddler taming*, said that toileting was one of the areas where children have the ultimate veto. If a child goes rigid and refuses to sit on the potty, then all attempts to convince or coerce them to bend in the middle and sit will be in vain. This applies equally – if not more so – to children with autism.

In addition to all the normal challenges of toilet training, children with autism may:

- have additional learning difficulties, so it may take them much longer to learn the basic skills they need to go to the toilet independently. It can take up to a year and sometimes more for children with autism to become dry, and two years or more for them to become clean
- have problems learning to speak and to use language. Your child may not be able to tell you they need the toilet in words, so you have to look out for other signs that they need to go
- find it hard to adapt from one situation to another. Because of this they may go to the toilet quite happily at home but need nappies at nursery or school. If someone tries to take them to the toilet at school they may become upset and try to run out
- become clean or dry, but not both. Sometimes children with autism will quite happily wee in the toilet, but refuse to sit on the toilet to poo. They may worry about getting splashed with water, dislike the smell or worry about falling in

- develop difficult patterns of behaviour around going to the toilet, such as smearing poo on the walls or on themselves. Sometimes this is a particular problem at night-time
- do a wee or a poo in other places as well as the toilet, seemingly without realising that this is inappropriate
- refuse to clean themselves after having a poo because they become very upset at the thought of being messy or dirty in any way. For some children with autism, this fear means that they refuse to move their bowels at all, become badly constipated and suffer from bad tummy pains and other symptoms
- hurt themselves by pulling at their genitals or digging at themselves either at night or when they go to the toilet.

Your child may experience one of these problems, a combination of them, or maybe none. But if toileting is a difficulty, read on.

Learning difficulties, autism and toileting

As with any skill, how easily toileting is learned depends on the extent to which your child's autism affects them and whether they have additional learning difficulties. It is common, however, for children with autism to experience difficulties with toileting. A survey conducted by one of our colleagues found that 82% of the children in her study had difficulties, or had previously experienced difficulties, with toileting.[3]

Your child's autism means they often have great difficulty understanding the social rules governing our lives – why shouldn't they strip off and have a wee in the middle of the park if they need to?

[3]Dalrymple, N. and Rube, L. (1992). Toilet training and behaviours of people with autism: parent views. *Journal of Autism* and *Developmental Disorders*, 22(2), pp265–275.

If your child also has learning difficulties it may take them much longer to learn a new skill. They may also take a long time to learn their body's signals – they may simply not realise when they really need to go.

How do I begin to tackle this problem?

There are two things that any parent needs in abundance: patience and a sense of humour.

Both of these are hard to come by at times. If you can hang on to these qualities however, it may do a lot for your sanity in the long run.

- First of all, don't try and make a battle of toileting with your child; you probably won't win and things may get worse.
- To tackle any toileting problem you will probably need to go one step at a time.
- Expect things to take longer than they would with children who do not have autism or additional learning difficulties.
- You are not alone. Most parents of children with autism will have gone through a similar experience. You'll find help on the internet and from local parent groups – for example, a branch of The National Autistic Society. You can meet other parents who may well have ideas that have worked for them and which might help you. They also really do know what it's like, and that can be a comfort.

If you find yourself at a loss about how to tackle toileting, you may be able to turn to a number of professionals for support and advice.

- Your GP, paediatrician or practice nurse.
- A disability health visitor, who may refer you to a specialist toileting clinic.
- A clinical child psychologist (your GP or health visitor may refer you).
- Your child's school or nursery. If your child goes to a special school or nursery for children with learning difficulties, or an autism-specific school, staff will have a lot of experience in teaching toileting skills. Mainstream schools and nurseries are also used to helping with toilet training. You may be able to talk to staff about things they are trying at school that you can try at home too. That can be effective because it means the problem is being tackled consistently throughout the day.

Getting help

If you seek professional advice, be honest about what you can do and cannot do. That way the person who is working with you can try and tailor the advice they give to your circumstances.

Very often when we seek advice about some aspect of being a parent, we go out of our way to create a good impression, because we don't want our seeking help to be viewed as a sign of being a bad parent. That often comes from the feeling that we are to blame for the problem. Parents sometimes do make mistakes, of course, but no-one teaches us how to be a parent – especially not how to be the parent of a child with special needs.

If you are feeling tired or down, or your confidence is at a low ebb, try and be honest about this.

It may be that initially, you need support to get you through a tough patch. Once you're feeling better in yourself you may be able to tackle the problem with more confidence. Confidence in your abilities as a parent is often part of the solution. The professional who is working with you may be able to help you directly or explore various ways for you to get support. There are a number of helplines that you can phone when there isn't anyone else to talk to (see Useful organisations on page 81).

Strategies to try

When it comes to toileting problems, there is no magic wand – and the strategies we mention here are not guaranteed to produce results every time. You may find your own solutions, but we've included some ideas that we've used in our work and that have helped parents in the past.

When considering any strategy, try to be realistic. There is no point trying to implement something that in the end you can't follow through, because it takes more energy and commitment than you have to spare. You'll end up frustrated and maybe angry and depressed.

Understand what the toilet is for

If possible, change your child's nappies in the toilet and show your child how to flush any solid matter away. You could say 'Down the toilet!' or 'Bye-bye poo!' to help get the message across. While they are still in nappies children can learn the routine of flushing, pulling pants up, and washing and drying hands.

Clothes

When toilet training a child, it is best to use clothes that can easily be taken on and off. If toilet training has been a problem, it is easier to tackle it in summer when clothes are easily laundered. You could use trainer pants to help your child become more aware when they are weeing and pooing.

Establish a routine

Like any child, a child with autism can be helped to get into 'good habits'. Take your child to sit on the toilet or the potty after every meal (this is a good time because the gut naturally seems to try and 'make room' for the new food to be digested by pushing waste out). Try taking your child about 20 minutes after a meal. Getting the timing right will be a matter of trial and error! At first you will need to take your child to the toilet at regular intervals throughout the day.

Look out for signals

Your child may give out particular non-verbal signals that they want a wee or a poo. These can be very varied; children can fidget in a particular way or go to a certain place (one little boy I knew would go and hide under a table when he was about to do a poo!).

Try and respond to signals by taking your child to the toilet and encouraging them to sit on the toilet or potty. Try and get them to sit for a short period of time, say five minutes, before you let them off. If they don't do anything, let them off but take them back a short time later, especially if they give signals that they are about to do something in their nappy or pants.

Prompting

Children with autism may not recognise when their body is telling them they need the toilet. Build toilet trips into your daily routine.

Rewards

Showing your child that you are pleased when they use the toilet or potty properly can be quite powerful. For some children praise will be most effective; for others tangible rewards work best, like being allowed to do a favourite activity, or being given something nice to eat. You will discover what works best for your child.

Don't encourage rituals

Some children will try and insist that specific rituals are followed when going to the toilet. Try not to go along with these for the sake of a quiet life. If you do, things can become more difficult in the long run. We once worked with a child who insisted on flushing the toilet at least six times after using it. Rituals like these are most easily stopped in the early phases; once they have become part of a set routine they are much harder to stop.

Smearing

Some children have particular behavioural problems around toileting. One especially distressing difficulty is when children 'smear' poo. They may do this at night in particular.

Smearing often prompts a very emotional reaction from parents as it is unpleasant and you want it to stop. However it is important to **keep calm**. Do not let your child think this is a good way to create a distraction in the middle of the night!

- Put your child in an all-in-one suit that makes it more difficult for them to access their body. Keep a good supply of disposable gloves for yourself.
- Show your child that poo goes down the toilet.
- If your child is old enough, they can help you clean up the easy bits.
- Make a photo book about pooing on the toilet or potty showing all the stages; read it to your child several times a day.
- Reward your child for not smearing.
- If you think that smearing is a sensory issue, offer similar sensory experiences during the day, for example make mud pies, use brown Play-Doh, make thick finger paint and draw on large sheets of paper or on a plain plastic tablecloth.

Special aids for more difficult problems

Some children have particular problems learning to be clean and dry and in these cases, special aids can help.

Alarms

A special pad is put under the sheets (if the problem is night wetting or soiling) or in the child's pants. If your child starts to wet, this triggers a buzzer or a bell. For children who wet the bed this usually wakes them up and they seem to automatically 'hold on' and stop wetting. These alarms are usually given out by doctors at special clinics for toileting problems, or psychologists who will explain exactly how they should be used. There are also special buzzers that can be put inside a potty to help teach your child to use it properly. Alarms are often effective when used alongside behavioural programmes designed to help you teach your child.

Mattress covers

If wet beds are a big problem special covers to protect the mattress are available from either specialist clinics or sometimes through your health visitor. Clinics and your health visitor may also be able to get other 'incontinence aids' to help you keep the washing down to a more reasonable level until the problem improves. If your local child development service has a special needs health visitor they might be a good person to ask for information about this.

Night suits

If your child smears faeces at night, you can get special suits which stop them from doing this or hurting themselves by scratching or digging at their bottoms. (Don't worry, it's not like putting them in some kind of straitjacket.) Alternatively, you can use any kind of all-in-one sleep suit.

Medication

Sometimes medication can help if your child suffers from constipation or wets at night or during the day. Your GP or paediatrician can advise you about this.

Obtaining aids, equipment and advice

Mattress covers and sleepsuits that help prevent smearing and other special aids may be available through a variety of NHS services. Contact your special needs health visitor or the practice nurse in your GP surgery to find out more. They will often be able to organise supplies of nappies for children who are delayed in achieving continence. Organisations such as Mencap (see Useful organisations on page 81) may also be able to advise what might be available and how to go about getting it.

Many local health services have toileting clinics which will be able to provide help and advice. The way in to these services will usually be through your health visitor or GP.

What if my child seems afraid of the toilet?

There are many reasons why a child with autism may not like the toilet. They may not like the smell (even clean, fragrant smells) or be afraid of the sound of the toilet flushing. They may not understand what is expected of them, but sense your anxiety about it. It is hard for some children with autism to change the way they do things, and they won't understand why they can't keep weeing and pooing in a nappy.

Try taking things in stages to overcome this problem. For example, if your child normally uses a nappy:

- let them come into the toilet briefly when other family members are there. Make sure the toilet does not smell of strong-perfumed cleansers (you can slowly reintroduce them at a later date). Gradually build up the time you spend there

- make sure the toilet or potty is the right size and easy for your child to sit on (use a step stool or a baby toilet seat if needed)
- try and get your child to wee or poo in a nappy or trainer pants while they are in the bathroom but not on the toilet
- then try to get them to sit on the toilet with the lid down while they are still wearing their nappy or trainer pants
- move on to sitting on the toilet with the lid up, and not wearing a nappy or training pants
- finally, try getting your child to wipe themselves
- after each stage, reward your child with something that motivates them.

This is just an example. It will be important for you to take your child to the toilet regularly, as part of their daily routine, and to try and remain calm. Change may be a long time coming – but don't give up!

If your child is afraid of getting messy or dirty, playing with things like Play-Doh, finger paints, pastry and clay can help reduce their fears. This may teach them that becoming messy is not the end of the world as they can always get clean again.

Summary

If we tried to cover every possible strategy or programme for every kind of toileting problem, it would be a book all on its own! You may find that patience, gentle encouragement and perseverance will in the end pay dividends. Remember that many parents find it takes quite a while. Above all:

- don't be frightened to ask for help, especially with distressing problems like smearing. The fact that there is a problem doesn't mean it's your fault
- children with more severe learning difficulties may need special training programmes in place for a while to help them become clean and dry. You can get help with this
- some children will learn to stay clean and dry if they are simply taken to the toilet regularly and reminded that they need to go
- really bad toileting problems are no joke – get support, help and advice if you need it.

3. Sleep problems

Introduction

Sleep problems are very common in children with autism.
There can be a number of reasons why they find it hard to go to
bed or to sleep. Here are some possibilities:

- fear of the dark
- fear of being left alone
- hyperactivity
- difficulty moving from one activity to another, for example
  from watching a favourite DVD to getting ready for bed.

Very often it is not the child who has a sleep problem (they often
appear to need less, or they simply catch up at other times) but
the parents. It is the parents who regularly have dark rings around
their eyes and look shellshocked!

It is good to get your child into a proper routine at bedtime, and
it's very important for you to get a decent night's sleep. If you get
overtired you can become impatient and irritable. Problems that
might be bearable at other times can quickly become too much to
cope with when you haven't had enough sleep.

Common problems

Bedtime tantrums

Tantrums can work very well for a child if they happen when
parents may themselves be tired and looking forward to some
peace and quiet. It can seem easier to let a child stay up longer,
play for a few more minutes, or watch a favourite DVD.

As with all the problems we discuss in this book, it is important to think about what your child may be trying to tell you through their behaviour. They might be telling you that they are anxious or afraid. Or that they are hungry, or simply not tired. If your child is afraid of the dark or of being alone, there may be some very simple things that can be changed to improve things:

- get a night light
- move your child in with a brother or sister
- leave their bedroom door slightly ajar so that they can hear your voices, or hear you moving about the house
- play quiet and soothing music in their room.

Here are some other practical things that you can do which might be helpful.

- Make sure your child's bedroom is comfortable and friendly.
- Keep favourite toys, objects and pictures of favourite things in the room.
- Use warm bedclothes (sometimes a heavy blanket helps if your child likes pressure from squeezes and hugs).
- Use blackout curtains that shut out all external light, especially in summer.
- Make sure your child is not hungry before they go to bed.
- Have a regular bedtime routine and stick to it.

Children with autism need routines to help them cope with a world they find frightening and where they often cannot work out what may happen next. It is important that home and school life doesn't contain too many surprises in the course of a day. Regular betimes, therefore, can really help. The build-up to bedtime needs to happen in the same way, if at all possible, each night. For example:

- have a small drink
- get pyjamas on
- clean teeth
- go to toilet
- kiss family goodnight
- get favourite soft toy
- go to bed and listen to a song or a story.

Things may not be organised in exactly the same way as this in your house, but it is important to have a routine. Try to be firm about the routine, however hard this is – if you give in, you are rewarding challenging behaviour. The more you give in, the harder it will be to change the behaviour in the long run.

Once you have followed your bedtime routine, **leave the room**.

Try very hard not to go back in to your child's room if they have a tantrum. Instead, see if you can ignore it. Remember that you may be trying to change your child's behaviour, but they may also be aiming to change yours! If you go back in the room and let them out of bed, they will have successfully changed your behaviour in the direction they want.

But what happens if your child gets out of bed and comes out of their room?

There is only one way to handle this – take them back without fuss or comment (the 'without fuss' bit is very important).

My child has violent tantrums, throwing and breaking things if we make him stay in his bedroom

We admit this is a tough one, but there are ways to tackle this – childproof the room.

- Remove easily breakable toys, put in lots of soft toys (you can even find rubber bricks in some joke shops) which your child can throw around if they feel really angry.
- Make sure the wallpaper has no loose edges your child can use to rip chunks off if they are feeling angry. Perhaps think about getting some wallpaper that you can paint over if necessary.
- Some parents have found putting a small catch on the door helpful. This prevents a child from completely leaving the room, while allowing them to see out. This may prevent you or your partner from having to do 'guard duty' outside the bedroom door – ready to return a child who tries to escape.

We are not suggesting you lock your child in their room – this may make them frightened. If your child continually gets out of their room you may have to stay outside for a while so you can put them back into bed quickly. If there are two of you, it may be helpful to take turns at this until things settle down a bit, and your child gets the message that they have to go to bed and stay there.

All children have to learn that being put to bed is not the end of the world and that actually, going to bed can be very nice. Having a firm and consistent routine is the best way to teach your child this. It is important also to make bedtime a quiet and soothing time. Common sense tells us not to get a child overexcited with rough and tumble play just before bedtime.

Watching a computer or TV screen until bedtime is over-stimulating and prevents good sleep habits. The type of light that is used on modern screens is known to prevent the normal slowing down of the body in preparation for sleep. Turn off the computer or TV at least an hour before you want your child to settle down to sleep.

Check that you are not allowing your child drinks and sweets that are high in sugar or contain caffeine. Both will prevent good sleep habits.

When thinking about bedtimes it is important to be realistic; all children are different, some need a lot more sleep than others. Some children also have naps in addition to sleep at night. If your child has a two hour nap in the afternoon and then bounces around until the wee small hours, it may be worth cutting down on their daytime sleeps.

Hyperactivity

Some children with autism are hyperactive. Although there is a group of children in the general population who experience hyperactivity, this condition is more common in children with autism and those with learning disabilities. In its most extreme form doctors sometimes give this condition the name hyperkinetic syndrome or hyperkinetic disorder. 'Hyperkinetic' comes from old Greek meaning 'too much' or 'over' and 'movement' or 'motion'.

If your child seems to survive on very little sleep (we know of one little boy who regularly got by on five hours or less a night and no daytime sleeps), it may be worth consulting your GP or paediatrician. Medication can be helpful in some (but not all) cases. Sometimes medication and a sleep programme can help you to make changes. Most GPs can make referrals to a sleep clinic.

Sleeping in Mum and Dad's bed

Individual families, and different cultures, have different rules about where children sleep and whether they sleep with their parents. In Japan, for example, it is normal for a baby to sleep between its mother and father at first. If your young child sleeps with you and it doesn't bother you, that's fine; if it does bother you, that's different. Parents can be troubled if a child gets into a habit of sleeping in their bed over a number of years. It's one thing if a toddler comes into your bed, but an 11-year-old is a different matter.

Many of us have our own ideas about the age at which a child should be in their own bed. If you have a certain age in mind, it's worth considering how you are going to help your child to make the change smoothly. Children with autism generally dislike change, and sleeping in their own bed could be a major change to their routine.

First of all, if your child doesn't want to sleep in their own bed, ask yourself why not. There could be a number of reasons: fear of the dark, feeling cold at night, not feeling very well or feeling insecure.

A few small comforts like those we talked about earlier – a night light, warm bedclothes and so on, may be enough to get things moving in the right direction. You can also consider the following ideas.

- Rearrange your bedroom so your child can't come into your bed on the side they usually do.
- Try and alter your child's bedroom so that it is harder for them to get out of their bed or cot and then sneak into yours.
- Try putting a wedge under your door so the child can't push it all the way open and get into your room while you are asleep.
- If your child sleeps in their own bed at their grandparents' house, try making a change the night they come back.
- Be firm and stick to your guns. If your child comes into your room, take them back to their own bed quickly, quietly and without fuss. Don't give up!
- Make sure they are comfortable; check their temperature, add or take off a blanket, offer a small drink, take them to the toilet or change their nappy if necessary, tuck them in and go back to your own room.
- If your child keeps trying to come into your room, keep taking them back. You may have to be prepared to have a couple of sleepless nights before you get your child into the habit of staying in their own room. If there are two of you (try and organise this programme at a time when you have help), take turns to take your child back to their room. Remember to keep eye contact to a minimum and make no comments.

Sometimes this can be a difficult behaviour to change. It can often build up over a period of time, particularly if a child has been ill and parents have taken them into their own bed to keep an eye on them and give them comfort. Later, when the child is better, they may refuse to leave.

If possible, try not to let your child get into the habit of sleeping in your bed in the first place. Make sure that they have plenty of their favourite things in their room. Look after them there if they are feeling a bit poorly, and make sure that a little bit of light comes into the room – possibly from a night light. These things can all help to make your child's room as friendly and comfortable as possible, and encourage good sleep habits.

4. Feeding problems

Introduction

In many ways the problems that confront us in helping a child or young person to feed themselves are similar to those that apply to toileting. One thing is clear with either situation – nagging or forcing does not work. As much as pinning a child to the potty and demanding they 'do something' will not produce good toilet habits, trying to pry open your child's mouth in order to insert a spoon will not help them eat properly. Sometimes without meaning to we can create feeding problems, because we are so anxious about our children not eating.

Feeding problems are not uncommon in pre-school children whether or not they have any form of special need. Some children seem to be remarkably healthy on surprisingly limited diets consisting of things like yoghurts, biscuits, crisps and milk!

While this should give us some encouragement, we need to think about what causes feeding difficulties for children with autism – and why these problems might persist.

There are a number of things that can contribute to a feeding problem developing:

- some children are very sensitive to certain textures or flavours
- they may dislike anything with 'lumps'
- they may be very reluctant to use cutlery and feed themselves, and prefer to be fed by an adult
- many children are very 'faddy' about food

- the difficulty many children have about being flexible often applies to feeding, especially trying anything new
- children who are overactive may find it hard to sit down and eat at a table.

Feeding problems may be maintained when you:

- try to make them do something they don't like or find difficult (for example, sitting still for a long time), or ask them to stop doing favourite activities in order to come and eat
- give your child a lot of attention if they are disruptive at meal times.

Tackling the problems

Be realistic and take small steps

If your child is unable to sit for more than five minutes at any task, you will not get from that point to sitting down for a full meal at the table in one go. Set realistic goals. A starting point might be 'Fred will sit at the table for five minutes'. Build up from this in stages.

Turn off the TV and computer at meal times and unplug them if necessary

You have to give the message that mealtimes are special times and separate from favourite activities. You could give a warning that your meal is going to start in five minutes, then three minutes, then one minute. Use a timer if necessary.

What is the 'pay off' for the child?

You will also need to think about what the driving force is behind your child's behaviour. For example, are they are getting attention when they leave the table? Perhaps you end up chasing them around the house to try and get them back. The best solution may be to:

- ignore them when they leave the table so they are not getting attention for doing this
- give lots of praise and positive attention for 'good sitting' at the table and eating
- consider a 'no sitting, no food' rule. Be firm about all meals, snacks and drinks being taken when the child is seated. Children regulate the amount of food they need very well. It is extremely unlikely your child will become malnourished.

My child is not interested in food and screams if I try and make them sit at the table

There are a number of ways to tackle this issue.

- First of all stay cool. Most children do not starve. Why not record how much your child actually eats over 24 hours; you may be surprised.
- Introduce new foods in very small portions and don't fuss if it is not eaten.
- Encourage 'good sitting'.
- Some children find being in close proximity to others in group situations, such as meal times, overwhelming. Try and understand this but don't ignore it. Sit them at the end of the

table, so they are not so close to others. It is good to practise this, as they will have to cope in small groups at school and sit down at mealtimes.

- Begin with a small amount of time your child is expected to sit at the table. After a short period of 'good sitting' allow your child to get down and do a favourite activity.
- Cut down on snacks between meals. Try not to give your child their favourite snack food after they've refused their dinner. Offer meals you are sure they normally enjoy and try fruit as a snack if they're hungry between meals.
- If they 'do a runner' from the table, do not chase them (do you know many people who didn't enjoy being chased at some point in their childhood?). Simply remove their food from the table to prevent them grabbing a handful or spoonful and then running off. Put the food back as and when they sit down.

Fussy eaters

- Gradually build up the amount and variety of food presented to your child.
- Do not force, nag or cajole.
- If the fussiness is due to a fixation on, or a dislike of particular tastes or textures, introduce new ones slowly. Try placing a small amount of new food (perhaps a few peas, for example) on your child's plate separate from a favourite food.
- Try not to fuss, and do not feed your child or make a big deal about them eating.
- Give praise after food has been swallowed, not before.
- Tough it out. Don't give lots of attention even if food is chucked on the floor (put a plastic sheet under their chair if you need to).

- At the end of a meal, just take the plate away without comment. Don't make a big fuss about what's been left.
- If you've tried to get your child to eat something new and it's been left, don't worry or fuss, just take the plate away.
- If you prepare separate food for your fussy eater, first give them a small quantity of what the family is eating. If they try this food, give praise after it's swallowed. Remove what is left at the end of the meal. If necessary give your child a small amount of what they normally eat and enjoy.
- Children behave differently in different places. They may eat happily at nursery but not at home, or the other way around. They may refuse food when they get a good reaction. Ever wonder why we struggle to get children to eat vegetables? Because we all panic when they won't eat their greens. Kids see our entertaining reaction and then, the next time they see a spoonful of peas, their mouth is shut tighter than a bank vault!

Other ideas

- Try and have regular routines around eating and avoid having different arrangements for everyone in the family.
- Think about using serving dishes or bowls of some kind. Give your child an empty plate and let them help themselves (younger children may need help). If your child sees everyone else eating while they're sat in front of an empty plate, they may think again about their decision to boycott that evening's offering, especially if they're hungry.
- Make sure that your child is hungry at meal times. If necessary, don't buy sweets and biscuits for a while: we know this is tough on other children in the family because it seems unfair,

but weigh that against dealing with the temper tantrums that occur if the biscuits are there.

- Cut down on snacks between meals.
- Wean your child off bottles at a regular time (usually before three years of age). Some children will not eat if they are full up with milk.
- Don't worry! Children rarely become malnourished because they refuse to eat. They eat more than you think.

5. Self-help: towards early independence

Introduction

It can be difficult teaching young children with autism how to take care of themselves. Sometimes they do not understand that they should dress themselves, even when they have the ability to do so. We tend to get dressed and undressed at busy times of the day, so it can also be difficult to find the time to work on these skills at home.

Forward and backward chaining

Self-help skills are best taught in small steps using a technique called forward and backward chaining.

In **forward chaining** you teach your child the first step in the process and do the rest yourself. This would be used for something like tying a bow. You concentrate on teaching the first step in the process until your child can do it. Then you teach the next step. It may take a long time to teach each step, but gradually your child manages to tie a complete bow.

In **backward chaining**, your child is taught the last step in the chain, for example when taking pants off you pull them down, then your child pulls them off. You may have to hook their fingers under the waist of their pants and show them what to do. In this way, your child experiences some degree of success. It is also a good idea to say 'Pants off', 'Shoes off' or whatever is appropriate so that your child learns to respond to a request and knows exactly what is expected.

Teeth brushing/hair washing and cutting

Some children really dislike having their teeth cleaned. For children with autism, this can be a bigger issue because they may feel that their toothbrush is enormous, or that it is scrubbing the skin off their gums. If this is a problem try the following.

- Experiment with various types of toothbrush and toothpaste.
- If they reject all types of brush and toothpaste, take a deep breath, use a small brush or your finger, and brush the teeth very quickly, rewarding your child immediately afterwards with bubbles or some other non-food treat.
- You could also try using a timer that rings after a few seconds. When your child is used to waiting for the ring and accepts a few seconds of tooth brushing, add a couple more seconds.
- Break it down into small steps, using your finger to brush the teeth quickly with water, then when that is accepted add a tiny, tiny bit of toothpaste and gradually build up from there. Or use a mouthwash if that is accepted.
- There are no easy answers to this problem, and a quick daily battle with a distressed child may be better than rotten teeth. Your child's resistance will pass and although you may find it exhausting and upsetting at the time, it is important to keep trying so that your child can develop independence and self-confidence.

The same applies to hair washing, although sting-free shampoo and lots of bubbles may make the task more pleasant.

- Use your child's interests to introduce distractions and rewards.

- Encourage your child to wet their own hair in the bath and make foamy bubbles. Or wash your hair as well as theirs.
- If your child dislikes the noise a shower makes and the way it feels on their head, wash their hair over a basin with a jug. Try not to pour water over their face and use earplugs if they are accepted or a plastic sun visor to keep the water out of their eyes.
- Wash dolly's hair together and make a little film or photo book if you are feeling creative and have some help. Play the film or look at the book regularly with your child (not just on hair-washing days!).
- Keep a special reward in sight and give the reward quickly at first (perhaps after a brief rinse), but gradually wash a bit more thoroughly.
- Give your child head massages at other times; this may help them to become more tolerant of you touching their head.
- If you have a son with this problem, keep his hair short. Daughters too may be better with shorter hair until they are more comfortable with hair washing.

Success in all these activities often comes when a child accepts them as part of their daily routine. Although it is difficult to keep calm when your child is distressed, if you can keep a sense of humour and be very matter-of-fact, you are already half way there.

Less frequent tasks such as nail cutting and hair cutting also call for imaginative solutions. Parents sometimes cut their children's hair while they are asleep as they are so afraid of having a haircut. It may not be a very good haircut, but it is better than having a struggle with a pair of scissors or hair clippers. One parent used to trim her young son's finger and toe nails by biting them, because he was terrified of the scissors. He will now accept nail clippers as his fears have diminished over time.

Take your child to visit the hairdresser and dentist frequently and build up exposure gradually before a 'real' visit. It would be rare for a dentist or hairdresser to object to this.

As with everything we have mentioned so far, break these tasks into very small steps and build up from there.

Washing

Washing is another skill that requires a fairly organised approach so that your child understands the difference between serious washing and water play. Bath time, if your child enjoys the bath, can be a great play opportunity. However, washing at the bathroom basin needs to be taught using the same step-by-step approach suggested above.

As we've mentioned already, it is consistency that is important. Your child will learn these skills in time if you remember these points:

- stick to your target and don't give up
- don't work on too many targets at once
- reward each success with loads of praise or whatever motivates your child best.

What usually happens is that after days or sometimes weeks of trying, your child will suddenly do what you want as though they knew how to do it all along. Don't forget to reward yourself as well as your child!

Step-by-step washing and dressing

We are very often getting washed and dressed at busy times of the day, so it is understandable that many parents do not expect their child to wash, dress and undress themselves. However, if you can find the time to teach them, it will save time in the long run. Keep things you need handy in a basket in the order you will use them, or check that they are all nearby.

Try using forward chaining: teach the first step then do the rest yourself. When your child can do it independently, move on to the next step.

Having a wash *(tick when done)*

Hands

- ☐ pull up sleeves
- ☐ put plug in sink
- ☐ fill sink with water
- ☐ wet hands
- ☐ soap hands
- ☐ rinse hands
- ☐ squeeze out flannel

Face

- ☐ soap flannel
- ☐ wash face
- ☐ rinse face

- ☐ squeeze out flannel
- ☐ pull out plug
- ☐ pick up towel
- ☐ dry face and hands
- ☐ hang up towel
- ☐ pull down sleeves

Getting undressed *(tick when done)*

- ☐ undo shoelaces
- ☐ remove left shoe
- ☐ remove right shoe
- ☐ pull left sock to heel
- ☐ pull off left sock
- ☐ pull right sock to heel
- ☐ pull off right sock

- ☐ pull trousers over bottom
- ☐ pull trousers to ankles
- ☐ pull out left leg
- ☐ pull out right leg

- ☐ pull up jumper
- ☐ take out left arm
- ☐ take out right arm
- ☐ pull over face
- ☐ pull over head

- ☐ pull up vest
- ☐ take out left arm

- ☐ take out right arm
- ☐ pull over face
- ☐ pull over head

- ☐ pull pants over bottom
- ☐ pull pants to ankles
- ☐ take out left foot
- ☐ take out right foot

Don't forget to praise or reward your child for each step they learn. Some children will learn very fast and move onto the next step independently. This system is good for sequencing the skills so your child feels confident and does not get in a muddle.

If you have access to symbols, a symbol strip showing the different stages of each task is the best way to show a child what has to be done and in what order. It will help them to become independent.

Learning to play

Many children with autism have limited play skills and are unable to occupy themselves in the way that young children often do.

If you have a garden, your child may enjoy swinging, jumping on a trampoline and riding a bike. Indoors they may have favourite activities and occupy themselves happily with little need for variety. However, sometimes the most favoured activities are those that are difficult to cope with in a limited space. Children may go through stages where they want to throw things, jump on the furniture, scribble on the walls or play the same piece of a cartoon over and over again.

While trying to keep these activities at an acceptable level, it is helpful if you have some time to teach your child something new. Start with a toy that interests them, maybe something they enjoy at school or nursery. Then spend a little time at least once a day teaching them to play with it. Maybe allow five or ten minutes and just have some fun together.

If you are looking at a jigsaw puzzle, use backward chaining to teach your child. Do the puzzle yourself and ask them to put in the last piece, increasing the number of pieces as they become more skilled. Show them different things they can do with toy cars, teddies, Duplo, empty cartons and so on. When playing, you can also teach your child the important skill of turn-taking by saying 'My turn' and 'Your turn' as you share a toy or activity.

Physical activity is also important, as research has shown that children who are given plenty of opportunity for running and playing active games are calmer and less likely to be challenging.

6. Coping with repetitive or obsessional behaviour

Introduction

Repetitive behaviour is part of autism, and is sometimes the result of sensory needs. For example, if the vestibular sense that affects balance is under-stimulated, a child may want to spin their bodies to increase that sense. Children who have difficulties with their proprioceptive sense, that sends feedback from the muscles, joints and skin to the brain, may seek out active activities like jumping and climbing, or may be unwilling or afraid to climb, jump, be jostled or even to walk downstairs. This is because their brain is interpreting the sense as either too much or too little. They may find some textures unpleasant to touch and refuse to wear certain clothes, or reject certain colours because they are too bright and hurt their eyes.

Repetitive behaviour can also be a safety valve for anxious children who have difficulty coping with change or understanding what is happening and why. It may also happen because a child with autism feels a strong fascination with or need to do certain things.

Obsessional behaviour may include a child's interests, activities or preferences. For example, jumping, climbing, lining up cars, collecting shiny objects, adding up lines of numbers, repeatedly watching the credits on DVDs, wearing certain clothes or colours and so on. Although this behaviour may seem unimportant when your child is young, it can sometimes impede the development of new skills and interests and become disruptive for the whole family.

Keeping things manageable

Increasing your child's ability to play and communicate more effectively will provide some alternative to repetitive behaviour. Ask their teacher, speech and language therapist, or an assistant at the local toy library (if there is one available) to help you think of ways to develop and extend a special interest or activity. For example, obsessions with spinning objects may be developed into a range of play activities with cause and effect toys, which can also involve social skills such as turn-taking and social interaction.

Obsessions with letters and numbers can be helpful in teaching early literacy and numeracy skills, and hours spent lining up cars could be the beginning of some creative imaginative play which you would like to encourage. However, you must be prepared to meet with resistance and angry indignation from your child if you start to change things too quickly.

Watch at first, sitting near your child, and then begin by joining in briefly. As they accept your involvement in their activity, slowly introduce new things that they could do. For example, if they spend a great deal of time lining up cars, you could develop and extend this play over several weeks.

Week 1: Watch, make comments, point to the different cars.
Week 2: Move cars a little out of line and 'vrooom' them up and down.
Week 3: Put one or two cars in a toy garage (this could be a cardboard box).
Week 4: Move the cars around the garage.
Weeks 5 and 6: Introduce ramps, roads, bridges. Have fun!

Self-stimulatory behaviour

If your child flaps their hands, spins, rocks or races up and down the room in a constant frenzy of activity, it will take considerable energy on your part to keep this behaviour at an acceptable level.

Children with autism often engage in this sort of behaviour because they crave the sensation, and it keeps them feeling calm and safe. If you are going to stop them doing it, you will have to give them an alternative activity to do instead. Your child will need to be taught other activities that provide the same sensory input they have been seeking.

For example, if your child spins or flaps their hands, ignore it at times when you are too busy to distract them with other activities. Try to distract them at other times of the day when you have time to do things together. If your child likes watching DVDs, and you have time to sit with them don't let them spin or flap while they are watching. Be very firm about it and turn the DVD off if they start. Say firmly 'No spinning' and possibly reinforce this with a gesture to show what you mean. Give your child something to hold that they can fiddle with instead. (You can buy specific fiddle toys online.)

Over the course of six weeks or so, build up a schedule where the amount of spinning gradually decreases each week until it becomes part of your child's daily routine: when they come in from school, for example, or when they go to bed. You could also allow spinning as a form of relaxation when your child is tired or unhappy, or use it as a reward when they finish a task that they don't find very exciting. If possible, get support from an occupational therapist, who will suggest activities that your child can do instead of spinning.

Other preoccupations

Some children have collections which they keep in a certain place or carry around with them. These may sometimes grow so large that they interfere with the daily routine. Again, draw up a schedule that takes you through the withdrawal process week by week. Reduce the collection by removing one item each week.

If your child will only talk about only one topic, this can be dealt with in the same way. Start by choosing a time when they are not allowed to talk about that subject, for example at mealtimes (if your child is happy at mealtimes and eats fairly well) or when watching television. Gradually increase the number of places and times when the subject is not allowed. Having said that, it also helps if you develop your child's knowledge about their favourite subject and broaden their perspective – in this way, it becomes a useful teaching tool.

You might find that it helps to use a sand timer when controlling obsessional behaviour, particularly for children with severe learning difficulties. Sand timers can be used to show the amount of time that is allowed for spinning or talking, or to time the gaps in between.

Sometimes children will stop a repetitive behaviour if you join in and do it with them, or attempt to change it into a game. You may not want to do this, but it is often very effective and well worth a try. Even if your child does not stop the behaviour, you are sharing their interests and you can gently change the focus over time.

If your child jumps on the furniture

This could be a sensory need involving the proprioceptive and vestibular senses. You could try the following.

- Find an old armchair that is for jumping on. If your child jumps on your good sofa, move them to the old chair and say 'jumping chair'.
- Take walks to the park or woods with opportunities to jump off tree trunks and bounce on springy toys in the park.
- Buy a big gym ball that is good fun to bounce on.
- Buy a trampoline if you have the space. It is possible to get them second hand or even free on internet recycling sites.

If your child scribbles on the walls

- Provide lots of card from the back of used boxes and packets, or cheap paper. Sometimes it is possible to get hold of old rolls of wallpaper free and you can cut these into large sheets and draw on the blank side.
- Buy washable pens or hide the pens until you have time to supervise.
- Paint a wall with chalkboard paint and provide lots of chalks.
- On a nice day give your child paintbrushes and rollers and a pot of water to paint the walls outdoors.
- Homemade Play-Doh, if your child enjoys playing with it, can keep their hands busy and provides some sensory feedback.

If your child climbs on everything

- Try to make sure the furniture is safe! You don't want a three-year-old child pulling a large glass cabinet over on themselves. Then decide where you feel it is safe for your child to climb.
- You may need to take your child for long walks or out to the park on a regular basis.
- If possible, redirect your child to another activity that they enjoy.
- Ask to be referred to an occupational therapist who can give you a programme to help satisfy your child's need to climb. A 'sensory diet' may include activities such as rolling your child up like a sausage in a blanket, giving squeezy hugs, or having a rocking chair or swing if your child likes swinging.

7. Unpleasant, destructive or dangerous behaviour

Introduction

Unpleasant or dangerous behaviour can include a wide range of things including spitting, chewing holes in clothes, tearing wallpaper off the walls, or throwing objects without any thought of where they might land. Worried parents have been horrified to find their child has lit the gas at 5am in order to make breakfast, or run a bath of boiling water in the middle of the night after wetting the bed.

In all cases of challenging behaviour, the strategies you use will depend to some extent on your circumstances, how energetic you feel and how well your child responds to things like rewards, praise, and so on. Children who are hyperactive will need a different approach to children who are fairly calm and have other interests.

Thinking about the behaviour

When considering how you might address your child's behaviour, ask yourself the following questions.

- How do I, and others in the family, respond to the behaviour?
- What function does this behavior have for my child?
- Does the behaviour fulfil a sensory need?
- Is this behaviour for attention?
- Does my child do this to relax?
- Has it become a habit, because they like doing it?
- What things could my child do instead?

- Could I prevent the behaviour by changing the environment or the way we do things?
- Is the behaviour a result of things my child finds difficult? For example, change of routine, loud noises, extreme heat or cold, or too much excitement?

Diaries

If you are not sure of the answers to these questions, keep a diary and write about the behaviour each time it happens. If it is very frequent write the time in five-, ten- or 30-minute intervals down the side of the page and tick the time when the behaviour is worse. You can then see if there is any pattern. If your child spends a lot of time jumping on the furniture from 7-10 in the evening, for example, they may need some exercise just before that time. An exercise bike, a trampoline, an old sofa or a run round the block may be a good substitute. Make sure your child has regular opportunities for exercise throughout the day, too.

When you are trying to work out strategies to use to help your child, it is wise to involve other people, such as older siblings or adults who play an important role in your child's life. Look at your child's strengths and interests as these can often be used as rewards or distractors.

A combination of solutions

Strategies often work on two or three levels, so you may have more success using a combination of solutions. For example, one strategy that can be used for dangerous behaviour is to secure the environment. Put a lock on the kitchen door if your child gets up early but at the same time, leave a snack in their room so they will be less likely to want to cook themselves breakfast. Here are some approaches you could use for other issues.

If your child jumps off furniture

If your child jumps off the furniture on to a glass-topped coffee table, remove the coffee table for the time being and rearrange the furniture to make jumping a little more difficult. At the same time you may decide to always say 'No jumping' when your child jumps, and to offer another activity instead. This could be something they enjoy such as listening to music, or something physical like swinging or riding a bike. You may decide to buy a trampoline or an old sofa and let your child jump safely on that.

If your child chews holes in their clothes

Try buying a chewy toy from a specialist shop or you may prefer to offer a very hard rusk or a soft toy made with vinyl or leather.

If your child only chews at certain times of the day, for example in the evening while watching television, you could put them in old clothes and ignore the chewing, or you could turn off the television every time the chewing starts. However, chewing is a sensory activity and it is likely that your child needs to chew and will do so, regardless of whether they are sanctioned. Deep pressure (massage, bear hugs, rolling up tight in blanket) can help if your child chews or tears their clothes.

You could also try substituting another activity. If you can stand the mess, water play or painting are two activities that are relaxing and absorbing for young children and may prevent them chewing. Waterproof aprons are also very tough and stiff – not at all chewable (though note that some children may refuse to wear them). You could dress your child in very strong fabrics that don't tear easily such as denim.

If your child spits

Children who spit will often stop very quickly if they are calmly asked to clean it up. This may mean holding the tissue in their hand with your hand over the top to clean up the mess, or giving their mouth a good wipe. Never show shock or disgust even if it has landed on your face, as that almost always makes the problem much worse. Just say, 'No spitting' and 'Clean it up'.

Spitting may also be a sensory behavior linked to taste or tactile senses. However, children often keep doing it because they enjoy the reaction it produces. It is therefore important to react calmly.

If your child wees in public

Here is a helpful case study: a child who, for no obvious medical reason, suddenly started pulling down his pants and weeing anywhere at school or in public places was dressed in dungarees or overalls. While he was attempting to undo the straps somebody would notice and take him to the toilet. If he was outside and had his coat on too, he couldn't reach the straps, so provided he was offered a chance to go to the toilet regularly, he gradually forgot his habit and began to use the toilet again in the proper way. After five or six weeks the dungarees were no longer needed.

Summary

Most problems need a similar approach to those already described in this chapter. You can:

- alter the environment to keep your child safe
- substitute something similar but less harmful
- offer your child another activity that is exciting but makes it impossible for them to do anything less acceptable at the same time
- use the same short phrase and physically stop the behaviour. For example, 'No throwing' and take away what they were about to throw. It is helpful to show a symbol at the same time and offer another activity
- try to make sure your child has plenty of opportunities to exercise
- if anything particular seems to trigger the behaviour, try to change your routine or avoid certain situations
- use 'overcorrection'. For example, make them clean up the mess if they tip or throw something. You will at first have to do it with them, guiding their hand
- help your child relax at stressful times by massaging their hands, feet or back with lavender oil, rocking together, playing soothing music, having a warm bath, breathing deeply and relaxing. All these things will help you as well
- praise or reward your child if they stop when you ask them to
- try to keep calm. Keep your requests short and direct. If you get angry it is like a red rag to a bull; the behaviour will become much more difficult to deal with.

Time out

This technique is used by many parents and is usually a simple 'Go to your room'. If your child has autism this approach is much more complicated. Your child may not understand why they are being sent to their room and they may become more destructive in their room where you can't see them.

However, if your child is doing something unacceptable and you are sure they are doing it for attention, then sending them to their room for a very short time (up to five minutes for a young child) can help when you have tried everything else without success. If their room is safe, and you can relax, it will give you both an opportunity to calm down.

Aggressive behaviour

Some children with autism find it difficult to be with other children or with adults. They find other people unpredictable and frightening, and cannot understand why they behave as they do. This can result in aggressive behaviour.

Like all children, your child may also be jealous of siblings but may not be able to communicate this or talk to you about it. Other things that sometimes result in aggressive behaviour are sensitivity to certain types of touch, sounds (some that you may not even notice) and specific colours or shades of light and dark.

Changes of routine may cause despair or fury, as will more specific things like an object being moved from a straight line. For example, a child once became very distressed and angry when the crisp packet he had laid carefully on a particular spot on the ground outside kept moving in the breeze.

Some children become so distressed they lash out at anybody and are difficult to calm. Others may push, poke, pull hair or bite. Unfortunately, aggressive behaviour can be very difficult to change in a short space of time, particularly if a child has limited means of communication. The two most important things to do are:

- respond calmly
- try to discover what is causing the behaviour.

Aggressive behaviour may, at first, be an innocent response to a problem but can become entrenched if a child learns that it causes a great deal of excitement, or a reaction. It then becomes a habit that is difficult to break. It's important to remember that children may be aggressive because they feel distressed. Respond in a very calm manner to avoid making the child more anxious and their behaviour more challenging.

You may have to keep a diary (see the section Why does my child do things that are difficult to understand and manage? on page 7) in order to understand why aggressive behaviour happens. The most common reasons are given below, along with some strategies that could be used. However, what you decide to do will depend on your knowledge of your child.

Your child is using the behaviour to communicate

Many two-year-old children ask 'Why?' all the time. Children with communication difficulties have to accept many things they do not understand. It is not surprising that they sometimes use physical and unsociable means of communication. Aggressive behaviour is guaranteed to produce a response.

If you think this is the main reason your child is aggressive, work with their teacher or speech and language therapist to help teach alternative communication skills. Your child may learn to sign essential words such as 'help' or to use symbols or gestures. If they are non-verbal, it is important that they learn to make choices by pointing or choosing symbols and pictures. They will feel more in control and be less likely to lash out in anger or frustration.

Your child may be using aggression to avoid something they don't want to do. For example, if your child hits their sister or brother whenever they are asked to tidy up their toys, they may be trying to cause a distraction that will result in the task being done for them.

The best response is to say firmly 'No hitting' and remove your child from the situation for a couple of minutes. Don't look at them or give them any attention. Comfort their sibling and then take the culprit back to finish tidying up. Stay with them in case it happens again. If necessary, help your child pick up the toys by holding your hand over theirs and guiding it, or tidy up together, which is much more fun. Give lots of praise when the tidying up is finished.

Your child is using aggression in order to gain attention

Say firmly 'No hitting, be gentle' and don't say anything else. Take them away without looking at them or giving any attention. Sit quietly for up to five minutes, and perhaps have a naughty chair or mat for a slightly older child. Afterwards, take them back to what they were doing or distract them with another activity but don't say anything else about it. Give lots of praise when they are behaving well.

If your child scratches or hits you when you are on the phone or doing something that you can't leave, like changing a baby, you may have to think of other strategies. Distract your child with a favourite toy or activity before the behaviour becomes aggressive, or find a way of letting your child join in. Maybe they would like to play with Play-Doh while you prepare the dinner, or bath a doll while the baby is having a bath. They could have a toy telephone for times when you are busy talking on the phone.

Biting

Many young children go through a phase of biting their peers. It is extremely distressing for adults as well as for the child that has been bitten.

Children with autism often bite to say 'Stop!' or 'Go away!' In school playgrounds children with autism may bite or scratch other children because they are too near, too loud or too unpredictable. At home this may also be the case, or it may be that something has happened that your child doesn't like and they don't have or can't access the words to say so.

It may be helpful to have an 'I need a break' symbol and teach your child to use it (or a 'Help' symbol may be sufficient). Or you could have a chewy toy and encourage your child to bite on it when they are angry.

If possible, try to avoid situations that are too stimulating for your child (for example, crowded playgrounds or noisy changing rooms at the swimming pool).

Your child is unable to share or take turns with others

Children with autism find it hard to understand why they have to share or why they have to wait their turn. These are skills that should be worked on at school and at home and progress may seem slow at times. However, children learn and it is important to introduce turn-taking into games at a very early age. An object, symbol or cap could be used to indicate whose turn it is.

Your child is reacting to something they find frightening or irritating

Children with autism may be very sensitive to certain sounds and certain kinds of touch. They may find some perfectly ordinary events really scary but not be able to say why. Some children put their hands over their ears as though they are in pain.

Ear plugs may help to block out any sounds that your child finds distressing. If your child finds certain textures difficult to touch, it is best to avoid them for a while and reintroduce

74

them gently. Sometimes children have panic attacks and may become very aggressive. If this happens to you, it is important to be matter-of-fact, talk calmly to your child and try to prevent them hurting themselves or hurting you. Regular exercise and relaxation are both effective ways of helping a child to keep calm.

8. Self-injury
Introduction

Self injury includes:
- head-banging
- slapping or hitting
- biting
- poking or gouging at eyes, and pulling at hair.

Self-injury is one of the most distressing and difficult types of behaviour for parents and carers to deal with. By its very nature such behaviour damages the child in some way, and it is this aspect that makes it so difficult to understand or sympathise with.

With this particular variety of behaviour it is important for parents to seek support and advice from professionals.

The ideas and principles behind dealing with this type of behaviour are the same or very similar to the ones we have outlined when discussing other behaviour problems. It is important to respond rapidly, effectively and consistently to self-injury and to ask a series of questions.

Questions you can ask yourself
What is my child trying to communicate through this behaviour?

You may not always find a clear answer to this question but if you can come up with some ideas it may help you teach your child alternative and more appropriate ways of communicating their needs.

How do I begin to tackle this behaviour?

One of the first steps is to think about the context: when and where does it happen? What is going on in the environment? There can be a number of triggers for self-injury:

- noise which your child finds overwhelming and distressing
- particular aspects of personal hygiene which are experienced by your child as intrusive and very uncomfortable such as brushing teeth, washing and brushing or combing hair
- seeking to avoid demands and control situations
- frustration at not being able to communicate their needs or feelings
- wanting to be left alone.

When a child screams and bangs their head in a noisy classroom, or bites themselves as soon as hot water or shampoo makes contact with their hair, the motivation behind the behaviour is very clear. The child is telling us 'I hate this' or 'It's too loud for me in here'. Once we understand this we can make changes so that the situation becomes more tolerable. For example, you might help your child to communicate their distress at loud noises by signing or saying 'Too loud', or putting their hands over their ears. This can be a cue for parents, teachers or carers to remove them to a quieter and less stressful environment.

You can also try and teach your child the skills they need to carry out as much of their own personal hygiene as possible, so they are not having their personal space invaded by others any more than necessary. They may take time to learn how to brush their teeth, and they may not like it much at first, but it may be much more acceptable then having someone else stick a toothbrush in their mouth. If they can do it themselves they will at least be in control.

What about times when I can't understand why they're doing it?

Sometimes it isn't obvious why your child is self-injuring, and there are no quick-fix solutions. Parents, teachers and carers have to carefully observe and watch what is happening when the behaviour is going on. This may give them clues as to why the behaviour is happening.

Ignoring the behaviour is not an option this time, is it?

No, it isn't. We must think carefully however about how we react. Young children may not be able to tell the difference between good and bad attention. Reactions of fear, anger or surprise may reinforce the behaviour.

A child should be given minimum attention for self-injury, and given a short, clear and firm verbal message such as 'No head banging'. Rewards for appropriate behaviour can be things like hugs and kisses and praise, or tangible rewards like food, drinks, or toys.

Give your child as much attention as possible when they are not self-injuring. This is especially important when they are using words, signs, pointing or gestures to communicate their needs.

Self-injury can be caused by physical discomfort, illness or pain.

If it is not clear why this behaviour is happening a full physical examination by your GP may help.

Summary

Self-injury is a difficult thing to tackle but there are ways of dealing with it. It needs to be responded to rapidly and consistently and your child must not get any rewards for the behaviour. Give them as much attention as necessary, but no more than you need to. However, give them lots of attention for positive behaviour.

Distraction may help prevent self-injury, especially if you know that your child finds it hard to cope at certain times of the day because of the number of people, the level of noise and so on. Perhaps give them a favourite toy to hold, or some time in a quiet place. Teach them how to indicate that they are upset or frustrated. Learn to recognise the signs.

Above all, if you are finding it tough to manage, get help. Go to your GP, your disability health visitor, speech and language therapist, child's school or whatever you can access. Do not feel ashamed or inadequate and do not give up! This is a serious problem and help may be scarce – but eventually, it will come. And don't forget parents' groups, whether online or offline, as these may offer good advice and let you know you are not alone in coping with a particular problem.

9. Looking after yourself

The activities in this chapter are probably the most important – and yet the most difficult – to find time to do. However, if you don't manage to look after yourself, and become anxious and exhausted, you will find it much harder to care for your child.

If you have extended family or close friends nearby, don't be afraid to ask them to give you some time. It doesn't need to be a lot: even just an hour a week of complete pampering can help you feel more energetic and positive.

You should never feel embarrassed or inadequate if you seek out respite care for your child for a short time every week or two. There may not be much available, as some schemes have had cuts, but apply for respite and chase it up. It is a great help in the long run.

There are also some things you can try at home:

- Write things down if you have the time, because a diary will show you just how much progress you and your child have made together.
- If your child can tolerate touch, it can be wonderful to lie down together while you give your child a massage. Lavender oil is very calming and many children enjoy having their hands, feet and back rubbed with it. This has the added effect of making you feel very relaxed as well. Many chemists and health shops sell small bottles of aromatherapy oils. Use a couple of drops of lavender mixed with almond oil.

- There are also some wonderful, relaxing CDs you can buy or borrow from the library with music that washes over you and takes you to a tropical beach or a cool, green forest. Children quickly learn to associate the music with being relaxed and this is also a very effective remedy for a less than perfect day.
- Try to organise a break or a special treat for yourself sometimes. Parents often remark that they feel guilty because they want to go on holiday and leave their child behind with a relative. However, this may be just what you and the rest of your family need. You will come back with more energy and everyone will benefit.
- If things are bad, ask for help. There is a list of organisations that give information and support below. Voluntary groups and organisations run by parents are often the best place to start.

Useful organisations

The National Autistic Society
393 City Road
London EC1V 1NG
Autism Helpline: 0808 800 4104
Website: www.autism.org.uk

Mencap
123 Golden Lane
London EC1Y ORT
Tel: 0808 808 1111
Website: www.mencap.org.uk

Carers UK
20 Great Dover Street
London SE1 4LX
Tel: 0808 808 7777
Website: www.carersuk.org

Contact a Family
209-211 City Road
London EC1V 1 JN
Tel: 0808 808 3555
Website: www.cafamily.org.uk

Professional help

If you need help, your first step is to speak to your GP who is able to refer you on to a clinical psychologist. Alternatively, your local health authority may be able to suggest someone who could help you. You can also find details of your local parent support group (contact The National Autistic Society's Autism Helpline on 0808 800 4104) and speak to other parents. They may know of a professional in your area who they found to be helpful.

Recommended reading

Attwood, T. (2008). *Complete guide to Asperger's syndrome*. London: Jessica Kingsley Publishers.
Available from www.autism.org.uk/amazon.
The definitive handbook for anyone affected by Asperger syndrome.

Baron-Cohen, S. and Bolton, P. (2008). *Autism: the facts*. Oxford: Oxford University Press.
This book explains autism in a way which is understandable, supportive and helpful.

Cumine, V. et al (2nd edition, 2010). *Autism in the early years: a practical guide*. London: Routledge.
Resource materials for teachers.

Gorrod, L. (1997). *My brother is different*. London: The National Autistic Society. Available from www.autism.org.uk/pubs.
Written by a mother of a child with autism, this illustrated book explains a child's behaviour in terms that young siblings will be able to understand. Aimed at children aged around 5-8.

Gray, C. (2010). *The new social story book*. Arlington, Texas: Future Horizons Inc. Available from www.autism.org.uk/amazon.

Griffin, S. and Sandler, D. (2010). *Motivate to communicate! 300 games and activities for your child with autism*. London: Jessica Kingsley Publishers.
Lots of ideas to help develop communication using simple everyday objects.

Hannah, L. (2001). *Teaching young children with autistic spectrum disorders: a practical guide for parents and staff in mainstream schools and nurseries*. London: The National Autistic Society. Available from www.autism.org.uk/pubs.
This wide-ranging book offers all kinds of tried and tested strategies to help young people with autism develop and learn. This title is due to be updated in 2014.

Hattersley, C. (2013). *Autism: understanding behaviour*.
London: The National Autistic Society.
Available from www.autism.org.uk/pubs.
Explains how to work out why a person with autism behaves in a particular way, and gives some strategies for managing behaviour.

Ives, M. and Munro, N. (2002). *Caring for a child with autism*. London: Jessica Kingsley Publishers.
This full and readable guide answers the questions often asked by parents and carers after a diagnosis of autism.

Moor, J. (2nd edition, 2008). *Playing, laughing and learning with children on the autism spectrum: a practical resource of play ideas for parents and carers*. London: Jessica Kingsley Publishers.

Powell, A. (2011). *Autism: understanding and managing anger*. London: The National Autistic Society. Available from www. autism.org.uk/pubs.
Explains why children with autism become angry, and how parents can cope with meltdowns and help their child to manage their feelings. Aimed at parents of children and young people with Asperger syndrome and high-functioning autism.

Savner, J. L. and Myles, B. S. (2000). *Making visual supports work in the home and community: strategies for individuals with autism and Asperger syndrome*. Overland Park, Kansas: AAPC.

Vermeulen, P. (2001). *Autistic thinking – this is the title*. London: Jessica Kingsley Publishers. Available from www.autism.org.uk/amazon.
This book has an original approach that evokes an appreciation for the strengths of the autism mind.

Wheeler, M. (2nd revised edition, 2007). *Toilet training for individuals with autism or other development issues*. Arlington, Texas: Future Horizons.
More than 200 toilet-training tips and more than 40 case examples with solutions.

Wing, L. (revised edition, 2003). *The autistic spectrum: a guide for parents and professionals*. London: Constable and Robinson. Available from www.autism.org.uk/amazon.
This book describes what autism is, how to help those with the condition, and the services available; a good guide for parents and anyone working with people with autism.

Finally...

Between us we've notched up quite a lot of years working with children with autism. Nevertheless, we both still come across children who throw us completely! We have to rack our brains and think of some way to get a situation unstuck. There have been times when the two of us have sat in a car outside one of our offices, having just visited a school or a family, wondering quite what to do next. In this way we can share, in a small way, the sense of frustration and being at a loss that many families live with day by day as they try and bring up their children – and prepare them for a world they may continue to find confusing and frightening.

You may at times find yourself stumped for ideas, too, and feel that you have tried everything. There are professionals who can help if you need them. Other parents may also be able to help; they may have a simple idea to try, or be able to think with you about modifying the strategies you have already tried. Your doctor or paediatrician may also be able to tell you about treatment if your child is showing hyperactivity as well as autism.

We hope that what we've written in this book may help in some small way, and make life just a little bit easier. Above all if you can believe that you are not entirely alone, and there are other parents, voluntary organisations, and even some professionals who do understand and want to help, we have achieved a lot.

We wish you all the best.